HEATHCLIFF PIGS OUT

The funniest feline in America delights millions of fans every day as he appears in over 500 newspapers. You'll have a laugh a minute as Heathcliff tangles with the milkman, the fish store owner, the tuna fisherman and just about everyone else he runs into. If you're looking for some fun, look no further, Heathcliff is here.

Heathcliff Books

HEATHCLIFF
HEATHCLIFF RIDES AGAIN
HEATHCLIFF TRIPLE THREAT
HEATHCLIFF WANTED
HEATHCLIFF SPINS A YARN
HEATHCLIFF DOES IT AGAIN!
HEATHCLIFF STRIKES AGAIN!
HEATHCLIFF ROUND 3
HEATHCLIFF PIGS OUT
HEATHCLIFF FIRST PRIZE!
HEATHCLIFF'S TREASURE CHEST OF PUZZLES
HEATHCLIFF'S PUZZLERS
HEATHCLIFF PUZZLE SLEUTH
HEATHCLIFF BANQUET
HEATHCLIFF FEAST
SWEET SAVAGE HEATHCLIFF
WICKED LOVING HEATHCLIFF
HEATHCLIFF IN CONCERT
HEATHCLIFF PLAY BY PLAY
HEATHCLIFF DINES OUT
HEATHCLIFF GONE FISHIN'
HEATHCLIFF CLEANS HOUSE
HEATHCLIFF WORKING OUT
HEATHCLIFF CATCH OF THE DAY
HEATHCLIFF ON VACATION
HEATHCLIFF KOOL KAT
HEATHCLIFF ROCKIN' AND ROLLIN'
HEATHCLIFF SMOOTH SAILING

CHARTER BOOKS, NEW YORK

HEATHCLIFF PIGS OUT

A Charter Book / published by arrangement with
McNaught Syndicate, Inc. and DIC Audiovisuel, Inc.

PRINTING HISTORY
Special Charter Book Club edition / April 1987

For information address: The Berkley Publishing Group,
200 Madison Avenue, New York, New York 10016.

Charter Books are published by The Berkley Publishing Group,
200 Madison Avenue, New York, New York 10016.
PRINTED IN THE UNITED STATES OF AMERICA

1-17
© 1981
McNaught Synd., Inc.
?
BEWARE OF DOG

"HE DOESN'T NEED ANY DENTAL WORK!"

PET
GROOMING
SALON
PET
GROOMING
SALON
1-20
PET
GROOMING
SALON

"HE MEOWS WHEN HE'S HUNGRY."

"CLOSER AND CLOSER...I STOOD STEADFAST...
SUDDENLY THE MONSTER ROARED!..."

"MEW."

"BUT I ALWAYS CLOSE FOR THE WINTER."

"YOU'RE GIVING THEM TOO MUCH EXERCISE."

"MY GOSH!...YOU'D THINK THEY WERE COMING RIGHT THROUGH THE LIVING ROOM!"

"THE CHAMP IS COMING IN FOR A WORKOUT!"

"HE ALWAYS LOOKS FOR THE UNION LABEL."

"A SHAMPOO, TRIM HIS NAILS, AND PLEASE REMOVE THE BIRD CAGE."

"HE'S DOING REAL GOOD IN KARATÉ SCHOOL."

"LEVEL WITH ME, CASEY... I HEAR YOU GUYS NAILED 'MR. BIG'!"

"AH, I SEE NATURE BOY'S BEEN BACKPACKING!"

"WE'VE GOT A CHURCHMOUSE!"

"AH MEMORIES!... AS CHILDREN WE'D MAKE ANGELS IN THE SNOW."

© 1981 McNaught Synd., Inc.
SPIKE
"WHERE'S THE CLOCK ?.... I'LL GIVE YOU FIVE MINUTES TO GET IT BACK ON THAT WALL !"
"COO, COO!"

"IF YOU KEEP YOUR MOUTH SHUT, SO WILL I."

"BETTER LOWER YOUR STEREO!"

"SONJA, YOUR VALENTINE IS HERE!"

2-16 © 1981
McNaught Synd., Inc.
"SEE THAT ?...IT'S A BLACK BELT IN KARATÉ!"

"I'LL FLIP YOU FOR THAT HERRING YOU STOLE!
...HEADS I WIN...TAILS YOU LOSE!..."

"ISN'T IT TIME YOU TOOK DOWN THE CHRISTMAS LIGHTS?"

" WE DON'T BELIEVE IN USING 'MUSCLE'."

"HE LOST HIS TOY MOUSE WHEN HE WENT THROUGH HERE."

"CAN WE DISPENSE WITH THE LEVITY?"

"HE WANTS TO HELP TAKE UP THE COLLECTION!"

"WANT A JOB?"

"SORRY ABOUT THAT NOTE, PROFESSOR!"

"I THINK HE'S FROM TEXAS!"

"FISH STORY!...THE ONE THAT GOT AWAY!"

"...WILL YOU STOP HANGING AROUND WITH THAT DANG HEATHCLIFF?!"

"HELLO ?... HEATHCLIFF'S ANSWERING SERVICE..."

"HE WALKS SLOW WHEN HE'S PACKING IRON."

"THE FIREPLACE SEEMS TO BE DRAWING NICELY."

"I DON'T HAVE MY TRAVELER'S CHECKS!"

"THIS HAS GOT TO BE SOME KIND OF A TRICK!"

"HE'S TRYING TO TEACH HIM THE SLAM-DUNK."

"CAN'T YOU HANDLE THIS WITHOUT THE BULLHORN?!"

"TUNA FISH!...IS THAT ALL WE EVER GET TO EAT?!"

"THINKING OF EXPANDING YOUR TERRITORY AGAIN?"

"HE'S GOT A CHOREOGRAPHER!"

"CONTEMPLATING A BIT OF CORNED BASS AND CABBAGE?"

"HE'S CLEANING HIS ROOM."

"MUST YOU POINT OUT EVERY DIVOT?!"

"HOW MANY SEED CATALOGS DO YOU NEED TO PLANT ONE CRUMBY LITTLE CATNIP PATCH?!"

"PRACTICING YOUR KNOT TYING?"

"TIME YOU LEARNED ABOUT THE BOGEYMAN!"

"SORRY TO KEEP YOU WAITING."

"HERE COMES MY MUSIC TEACHER."

3-28 © 1981
McNaught Synd., Inc.
BEWARE OF DOG
BEWARE OF DI
BEWARE OF DING
?
BEWAR OF DIN
DING!

"DOCTOR LIVINGSTONE, I PRESUME?!"

4-2
© 1981 McNaught Synd., Inc.
Elite FISH MARKET
BUILDING COMING DOWN
LAST DAYS
GOING OUT OF BUSINESS
MUST VACATE
FINAL SALE
Elite FISH MARKET
BUILDING COMING DOWN
LAST DAYS
GOING OUT OF BUSINESS
MUST VACATE
FINAL SALE

"HE'D LIKE TO ENTER AS A 'NON-WORKING' BREED."

"WHAT ABOUT SECURITY, YOU MIGHT ASK...."

"HE ALWAYS SENDS OUT FOR A PIZZA!"

"WHAT HAPPENED, CAESAR?"

"NOT DURING THE NATIONAL ANTHEM!"

© 1981 McNaught Synd., Inc.
4-9
"WAIT'LL IT'S AT THE CURB!"

"FABULOUS STRING COLLECTION YOU'VE GOT THERE!"

"YOU SHOULDN'T HAVE PUT HEATHCLIFF OUT... I HEAR HIM AT THE WINDOW."

"I HATE REVIEWING LAST WEEK'S FILMS!"

"SORRY, PAL... THE CUPBOARD IS BARE!"

"AN EASTER BOUQUET!... FOR ME?!!"

"WILBUR ..?... NO, YOU MUST BE ORVILLE...."

4-15
© 1981 McNaught Synd., Inc.
"I'VE GOT HIM BELIEVING THERE REALLY **IS** AN OGRE DOWN THERE.... HEE, HEE!... HE WANTS TO GO SEE HIM!"
INTERNAL REVENUE
"HEE, HEE!"

"THIS IS REALLY FUN!... HUNTING FOR EASTER EGGS!"

"IT KEEPS THE CROWS OUT OF HIS CATNIP PATCH."

"ONCE AGAIN YOU'VE INSULTED MY MUSIC TEACHER!"

"HE'S BEEN BANNED FROM THE ROLLER RINK!"

"SORE LOSER!"

"WELL, ***SOMEBODY*** ORDERED THIS SCRATCHING POST!"

"IF YOU'RE GOING TO DIET, THAT'S YOUR PROBLEM!"

"HE HAS A SPECIAL WAY WITH THOSE BAD-TEMPERED PLAYERS."

"NOW, QUIT THAT!"

"WE THOUGHT MILITARY SCHOOL
MIGHT KEEP HIM OUT OF TROUBLE."

"DID THE HEATHCLIFF MARATHON GO BY HERE?"

"HE WANTS A SECOND OPINION."

"THOSE HEADPHONES ARE CRUSHING YOUR BONNET!"

"I HATE THESE FIRE DRILLS!"

"HEATHCLIFF'S CATNIP PATCH WON A RIBBON FROM THE GARDEN CLUB!"

"IT NEVER FAILS!...GET IN THE TUB AND THE PHONE RINGS."

"IT'S OUR $200 DELUXE SCRATCHING POST!"

"LET'S SEE...THAT'S ONE FROM COLUMN 'A', ONE FROM COLUMN 'B', AND ONE FROM COLUMN 'C'."

"BETTER GET THAT HOTSHOT IN THE PENTHOUSE!"

"HE SEEMS TO HAVE A WAY WITH FISH!"

"THAT'S NOT A SCRATCHING POST... IT'S AN ALUMINUM BAT!"

"I DON'T NEED A LID ON IT!"

© 1981
McNaught Synd., Inc.
5-18

"HE'S GONNA BE DISQUALIFIED!"

6-20
© 1981 McNaught Synd., Inc.

"CAN'T EVEN TAKE FIVE MINUTES FOR A SHORT BEER!"

"HAD YOU PLANNED ON ELOPING WITH CRAZY SHIRLEY?"

"HELLO ?...'GARBAGE DUMPERS ANONYMOUS.'...HOTLINE."

"YOU JUST SAT THERE AND LET HIM RUN THE HOSE ?!"

5-26
© 1981 McNaught Synd., Inc.
GUM
GUM
"HE LOST A QUARTER DOWN THE GRATE."

"I'D LIKE TO THANK MY FELLOW DOGCATCHERS FOR THIS GOLD WATCH, AND HEATHCLIFF FOR THE CAN OF TUNA!"

"YOU GONNA BLAME ME FOR A RAIN DELAY?!"

"AT LAST! THE CONCERT IS ENDING!....

...HIS CLEAN-UP CREW IS HERE."

"STUPID!...DON'T HIDE IN THE PIRATE SHIP!"

"SO MUCH FOR DIPLOMATIC IMMUNITY!"

" YOUR NIGHTSTICK ?...IT'S OVER HERE."

"TIME YOU PUT UP THE SCREENS!"

"IT'S A SCOUT FROM THE YANKEES!"

"WHAT HAVE YOU DONE THIS TIME ?!"

"THANKS FOR SAVING ME A SPACE!"

"I'M GLAD I INSTALLED AN AIR BAG!"

"HAND ME EVERYTHING BUT YOUR CAT!"

"THAT POOL WAS A MISTAKE!"

6-10

"WHERE WERE YOU WHEN THEY ADDED A GREENHOUSE?!"

"THAT'S HIS NEW SWORD IN A SCRATCHING POST!"

"EGAD!...THE DODO BIRD!...RARE!...SELDOM SEEN!...

....IN FACT, EXTINCT!"

"HE INSISTS ON THE LOWER BUNK!"

6-16

NO
PETS
ALLOWED
ON THE
BEACH

"NEXT."

"NET!"
6-18
© 1981 McNaught Synd., Inc.
"THANKS!"

"HE'S GOT A LOT OF FAMILY ON THE PAYROLL!"

6·20
© 1981
McNaught Synd., Inc.
SPIKE
SPIKE
SPIKE
SPIKE

"ARE YOU RIDING 'PRETTY KITTY'?"

"WILL YOU QUIT THAT SNORING ?!"

"HE TOOK TIME OUT FROM A VERY BUSY SCHEDULE JUST TO BE HERE!"

"WHAT HAPPENED, WINKY?"

"SIT DOWN AND FINISH YOUR MEAL!"

"AND HIS WATERPROOF WATCH IS STILL TICKING!"